CONTENTS

KT-394-256

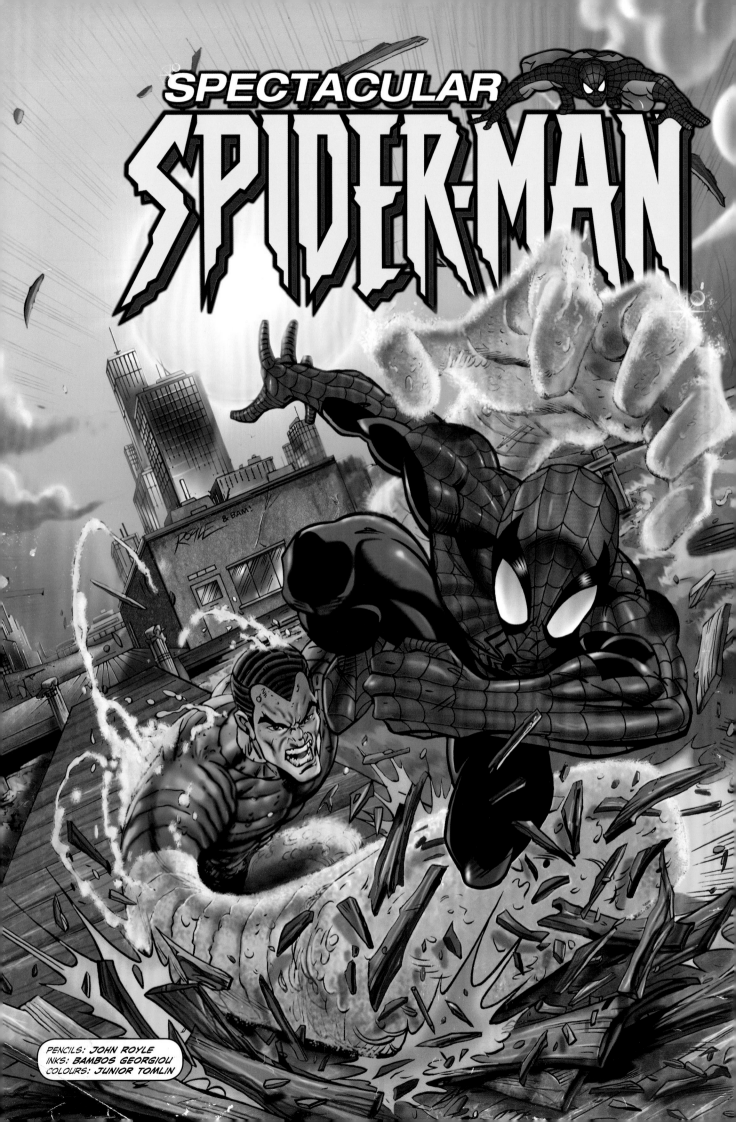

SCRIPT: FERG HANDLEY PENCILS: JON HAWARD INKS: BAMBOS GEORGIOU
COLOURS: DAVE WINDETT LETTERS: CAROLINE DUNK EDITOR: TOM O'MALLEY

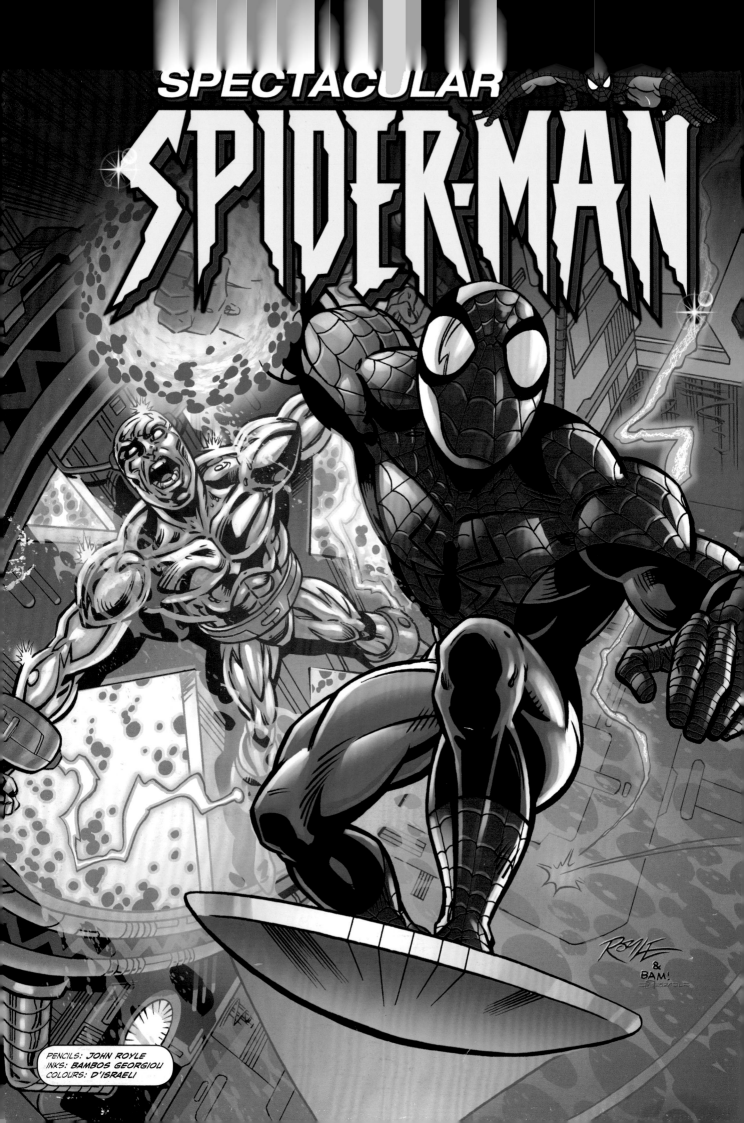

ONCE THE HERALD OF GALACTUS, THE *SILVER SURFER*
REBELLED AGAINST HIS MASTER TO SAVE THE PLANET EARTH.
NOW HE ROAMS THE LONELY SPACE LANES, PROTECTING
HUMANITY WITH THE MIGHT OF THE *POWER COSMIC.*

SPACE RACE!

BUT THIS NIGHT, TERRIBLE DANGER LURKS...

...IN THE SHAPE OF *KANG THE CONQUEROR,*
WARLORD OF THE *31st* CENTURY...

PERFECT! MY
SPECIALLY-DESIGNED
HYPER-CANNON HAS FELLED
THE SILVER ONE -- AND NOW
THE WORLD IS *MINE* FOR
THE TAKING!

SHOOOOMMM

SCRIPT: FERG HANDLEY
PENCILS: JON HAWARD
INKS: DAVID ROACH
COLOURS: DYLAN TEAGUE
LETTERS: TIM WARRAN-SMITH
EDITOR: ED HAMMOND

29

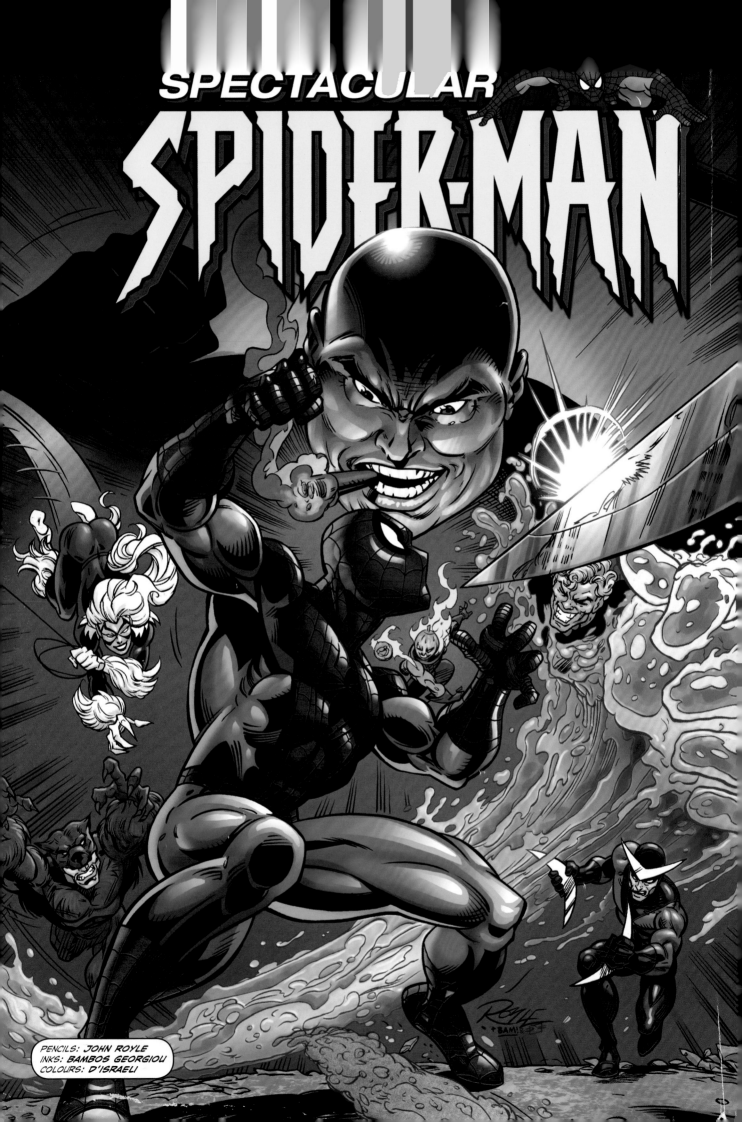

WILSON FISK - IS **THE KINGPIN** - IS ANGRY. A RECENT RUN-IN WITH **SPIDER-MAN** AND **SILVER SABLE** SAW HIM LOSING MILLIONS OF DOLLARS TO CHARITY; THUS WEAKENING HIS POSITION AS NEW YORK'S CRIME LORD.

"...RAIDING MY CLUBS AND GAMBLING DENS, EVEN ROBBING MY COURIERS IN BROAD DAYLIGHT..."

"NATURALLY, I HAVE TAKEN STEPS, SUCH AS HIRING THE SHOCKER ..."

THAT WAS JUST A WARNING, **HAMMERHEAD**. LAY OFFA THE KINGPIN'S TERRITORY IF YA KNOW WHAT'S GOOD FOR YA.

IT'S MADDENING. RIVALS LIKE HAMMERHEAD THINK I'VE GONE SOFT AND HAVE STARTED MUSCLING IN ON MY OPERATIONS...

"HOWEVER, I STILL NEED TO STOP THE ROT. WHICH IS WHY I HAVE DECIDED TO TAKE PUBLIC - AND PERMANENT - REVENGE ON **SPIDER-MAN**..."

SHAME ON YOU BOYS, TRYING TO STEAL THAT POOR WOMAN'S HANDBAG.

LOOK OUT --

AAAARGH!

BOUNTY HUNT!

SCRIPT: **FERG HANDLEY**   PENCILS: **JON HAWARD**
INKS: **DAVID ROACH**   COLOURS: **DYLAN TEAGUE**
LETTERS: **NEIL PORTER**   EDITOR: **ED HAMMOND**

THURSDAY...

THIS IS GETTING RIDICULOUS. I'VE JUST BEEN AMBUSHED BY FROG-MAN. *FROG-MAN*, FOR CRYING OUT LOUD!

FRIDAY NIGHT.

WOW, I'VE BEEN OUT A *WHOLE* TWO HOURS WITHOUT BEING ATTACKED.

HOLD ON, SPIDER-SENSE --

OTHERS MAY HAVE FAILED, SPIDER-MAN, BUT NOT *JACK-O-LANTERN!*

AAAARGH-- MY ARM!

GAS BOMBS...CAN'T DODGE...

UGHNN!

SLEEPING LIKE A BABY, NOW NOTHING CAN STOP ME FROM CLAIMING THE BOUNTY --

AH HA HA HA!

THE KINGPIN'S MANSION, WESTCHESTER COUNTY.

LOOK BOSS, IT'S JACK-O-LANTERN -- AND HE'S GOT THE *GOODS!*

INDEED, SHOCKER. THOUGH I THOUGHT IT'D BE SOMEONE MORE POWERFUL THAT CAPTURED HIM, LIKE *CARNAGE* OR THE *HOBGOBLIN.*

BUT AS THE GLIDER LANDS, THE HELMET COMES OFF TO REVEAL THE URBAN VIGILANTE KNOWN AS...

THE *PUNISHER!* BUT HOW?

HAD TO PUT A STOP TO THIS WHACKO BOUNTY HUNT OF YOURS, CHUBBY...

"...SO I WENT ON THE TRAIL. IT TOOK TIME, BUT THEN I SAW SPIDER-MAN BEING CAPTURED BY PUMPKIN-HEAD JACK..."

OH, AND I'M FEELING *MUCH* BETTER NOW. THANKS FOR ASKING, BLUBBER-PUSS.

"ALL IT TOOK WAS A WELL-AIMED STUN GRENADE..."

...AND I'M SURE YOU CAN FIGURE OUT THE REST.

GET THEM!!!

47

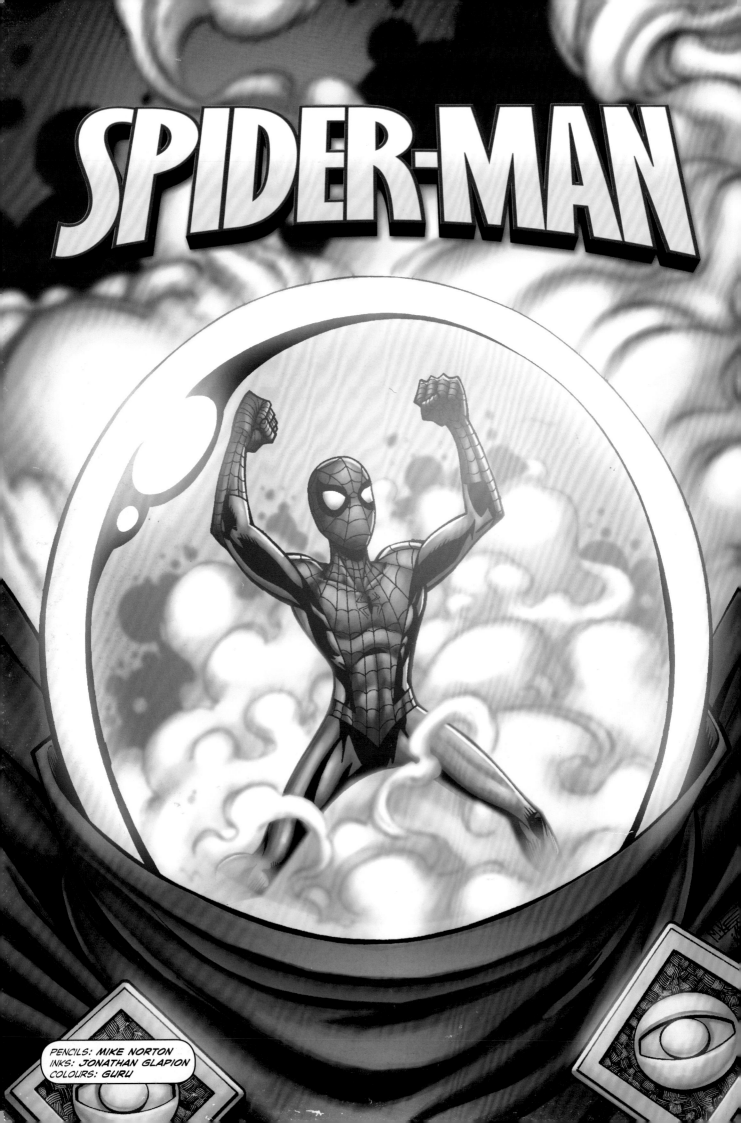

SPIDER-MAN

PENCILS: MIKE NORTON
INKS: JONATHAN GLAPION
COLOURS: GURU

SCRIPT: SEAN McKEEVER   PENCILS: MIKE NORTON   INKS: JONATHAN GLAPION   COLOURS: GURU
EFX'S HARTMAN AND BEVARD   LETTERS: DAVE SHARPE   ASSISTANT EDITOR: NATHAN COSBY
EDITOR: MACKENZIE CADENHEAD   CONSULTING EDITOR: MARK PANICCIA   CHIEF: JOE QUESADA
ADAPTED AND EDITED BY GABRIELE PANINI

TAKE THIS!

OOF!

THUD!

AND THIS!

DUNNO HOW HE'S DOING THIS --

-- BUT I'M A SITTING DUCK - I'VE GOTTA GET OUTTA HERE!

NOTHING'S HURT TOO BAD, I GUESS...

...EXCEPT MY PRIDE!

THANK YOU, THANK YOU!

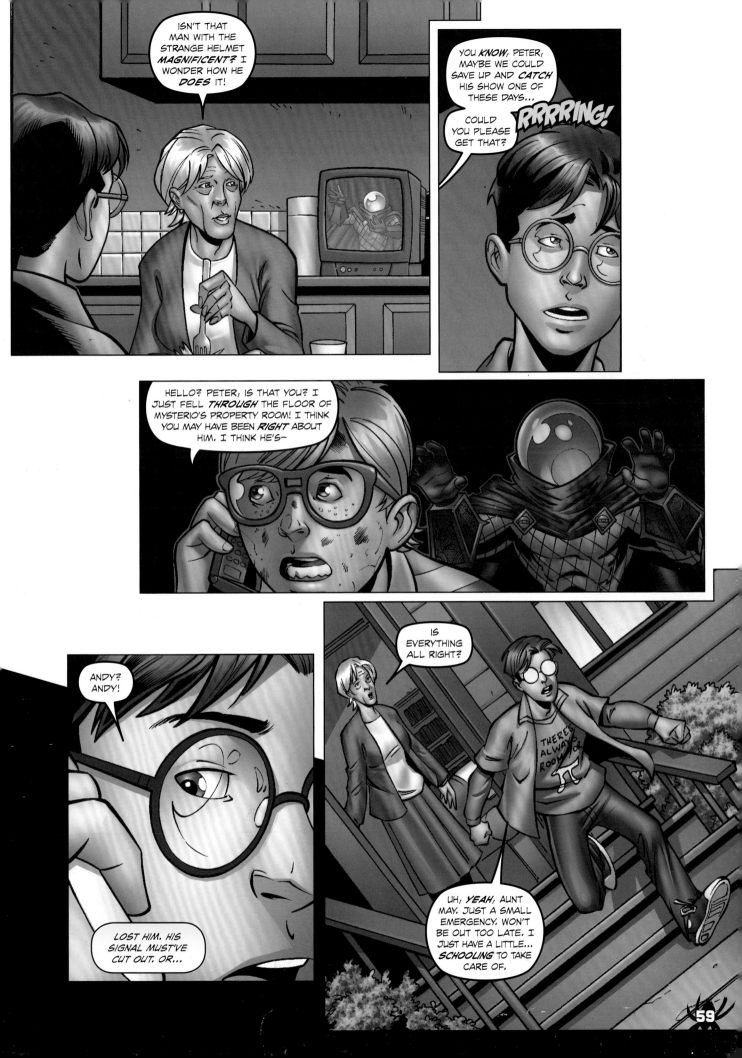